Jamaican ABC with Auntie Olivia

Written by Olivia Carter
Illustrated by Pete McDaniel

Auntie Olivia would like to dedicate this book to her mom, Rosalee, her dad, Andrew, and her family who have given her the freedom to dream and to be, to her brave and strong grandmother, Ms. Ethel, and to her dearly missed grandmother and family matriarch Petrona, on whose shoulders we all stand.

auntieolivia@jamaicanabc.com

First paperback edition November 2022

Book design by Olivia Carter
Illustration by Pete McDaniels

ISBN 978-976-96987-1-0

www.jamaicanabc.com

Jamaican ABC

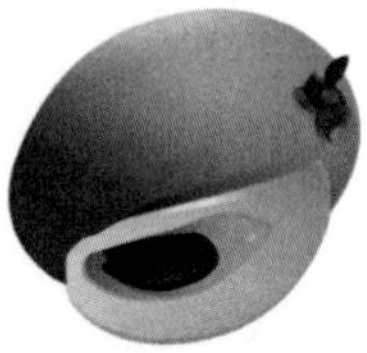

Hello, friend!
Let's learn our ABCs with Jamaican fruits and vegetables?
LET'S GO!

A is for

ackee

Ackee is Jamaica's national fruit.

B is for

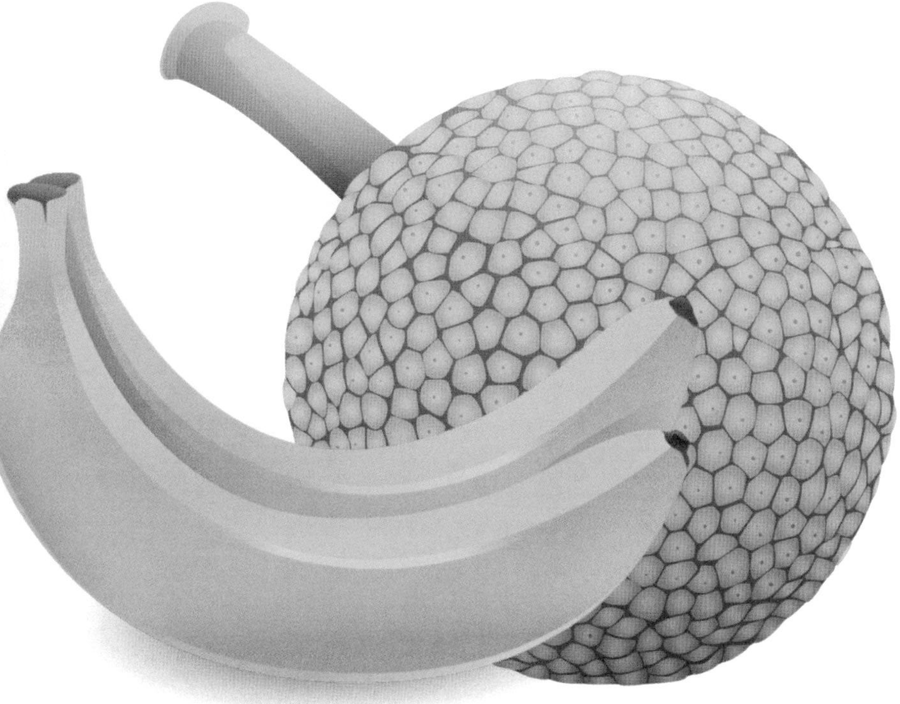

banana

We eat them when green or yellow, just like breadfruit.

C is for

carambola

C is for coconut.

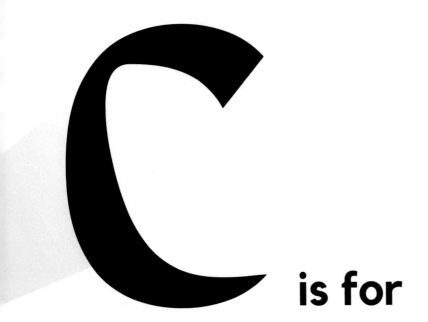

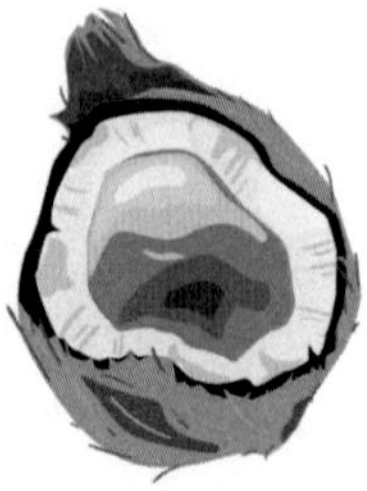

D is for

dasheen

Before you eat it, cook it in a pot.

E is for

elderberries

Elderberries are not so big.

F is for

fig

They are our native Jamaican figs.

G is for

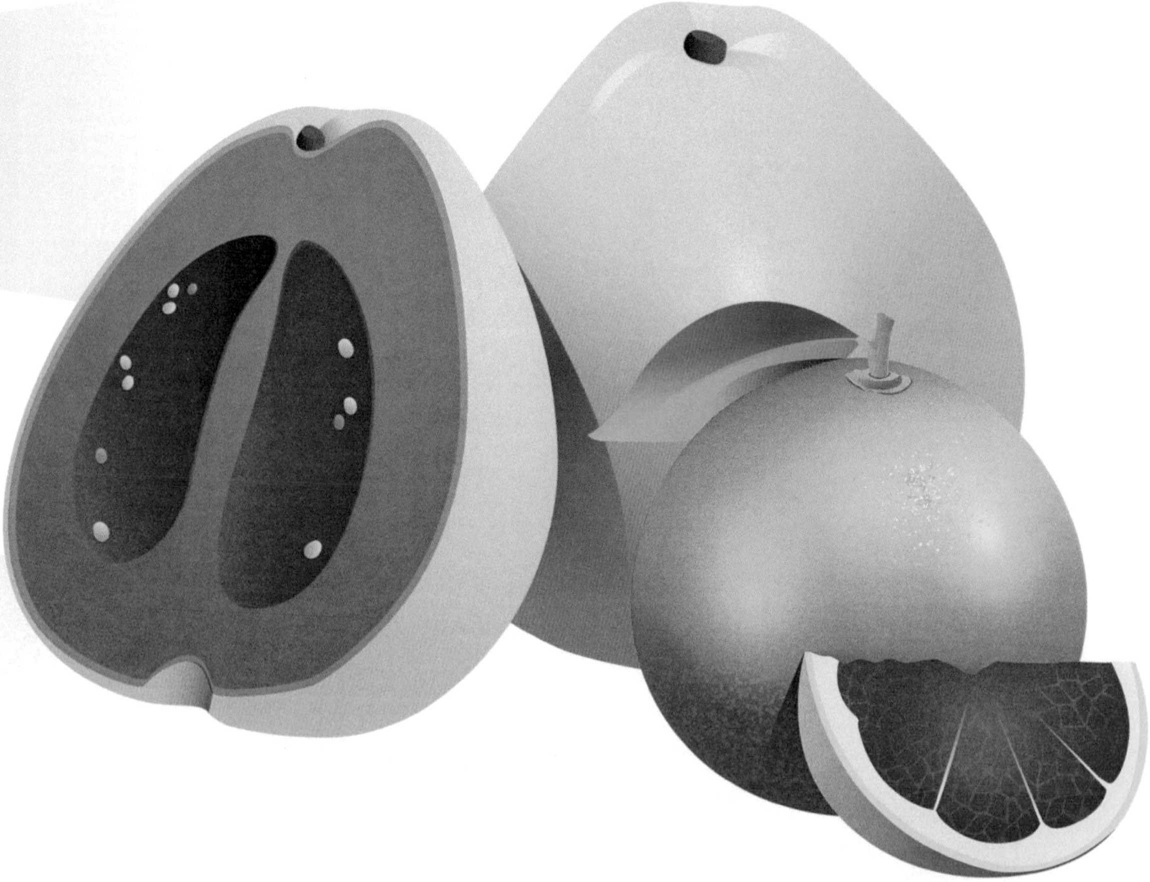

guava

G is for grapefuit too.

H is for

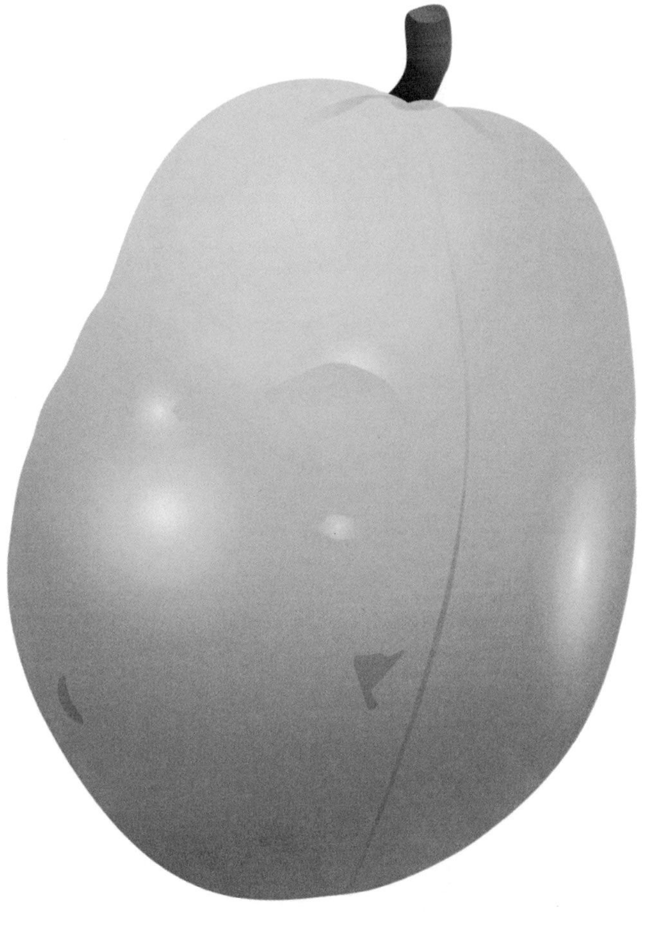

hogplum

I have many to share with you.

I is for

icecream

We make it with soursop.

J is for

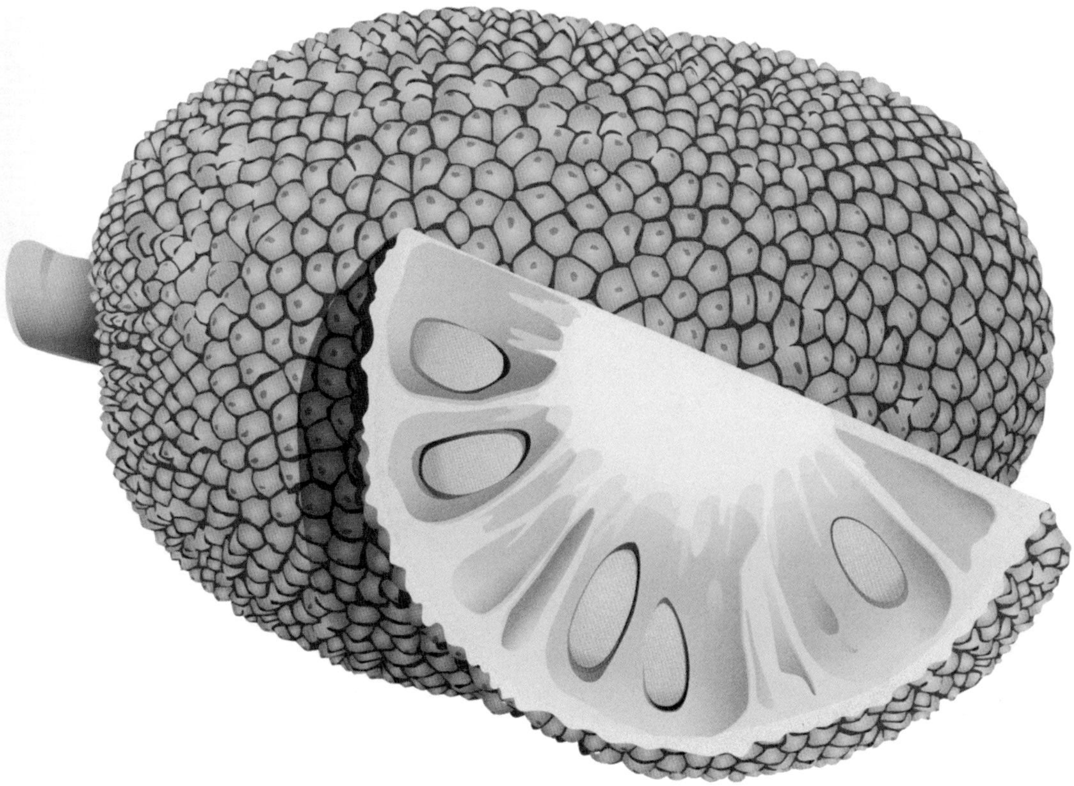

jackfruit

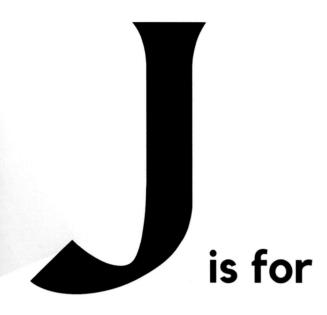

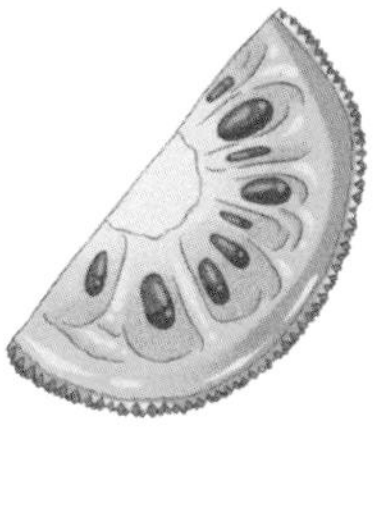

When I eat it, I can't stop.

K is for

kidney beans

We use it for rice and peas. 

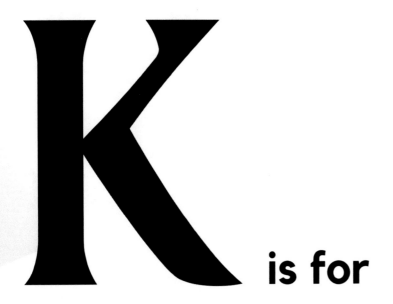

L is for

lychee

It came to us from the Chinese.

Out of many, one people.

M is for

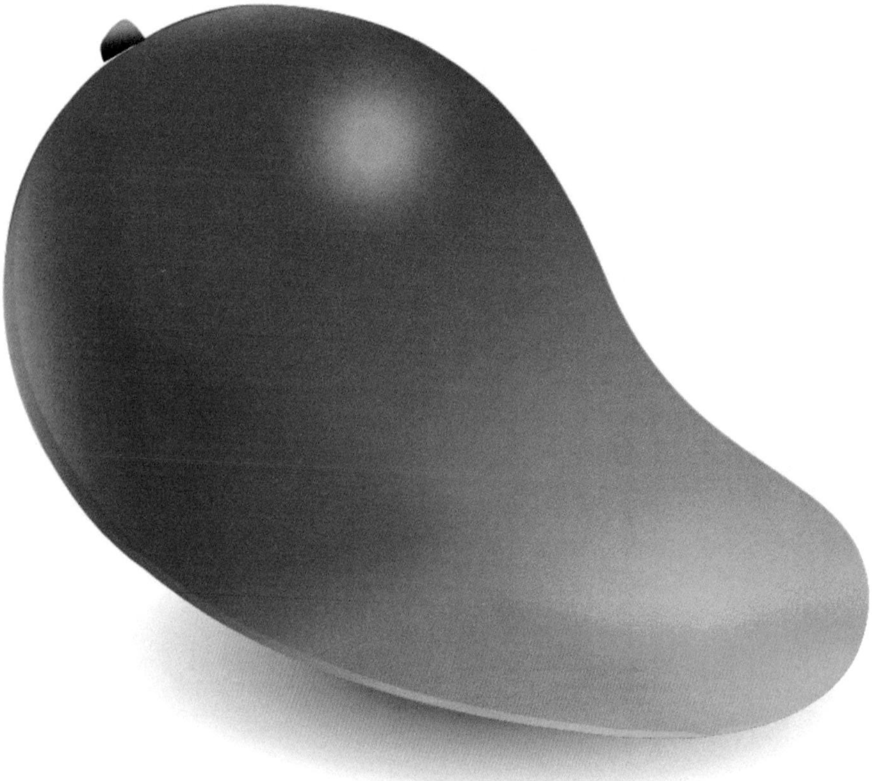

mango

I like St. Julian mangoes and Bombay.

N is for

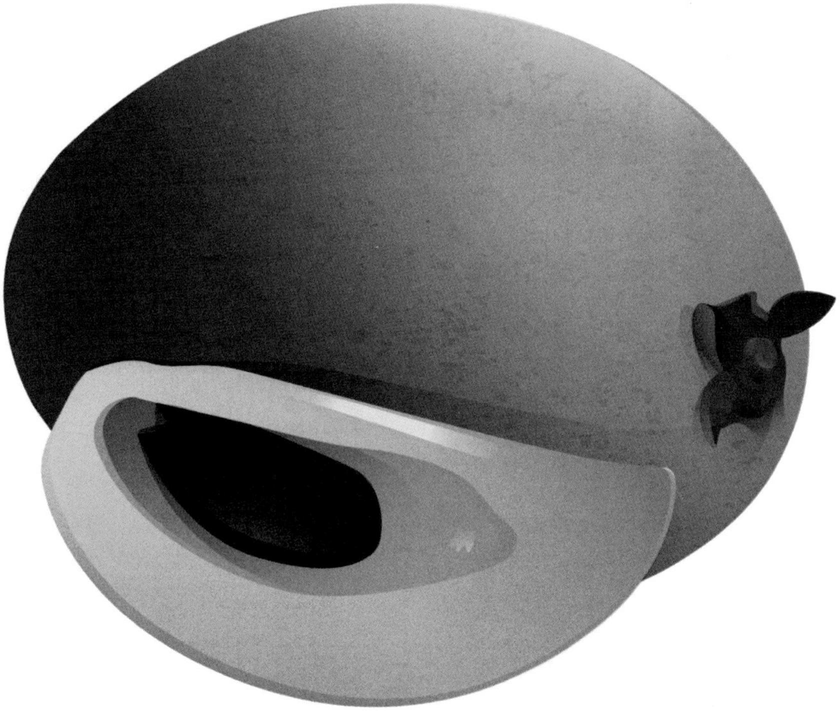

naseberry

I can eat them every day.

O is for

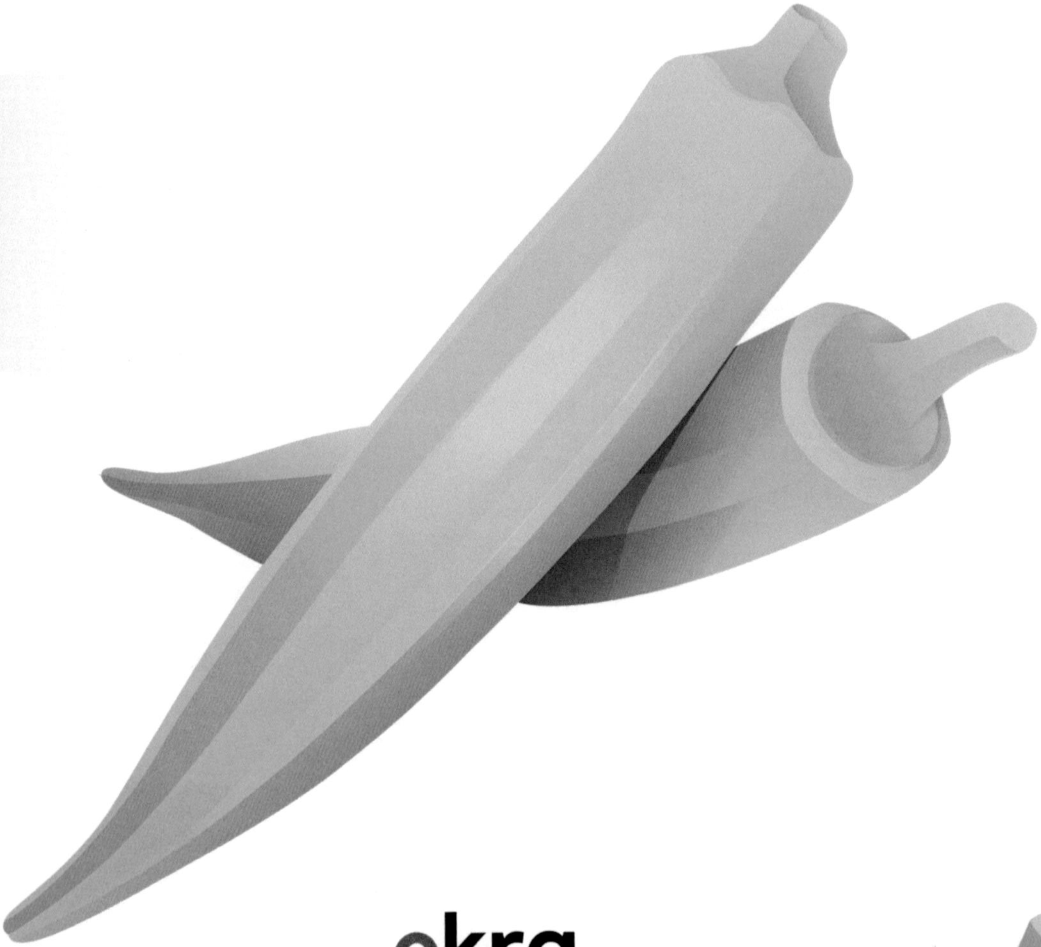

okra

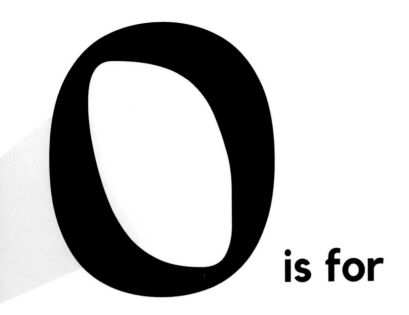

It is a very healthy vegetable.

P is for

passion fruit

P is for the delicious pineapple.

Q is for

quenepa

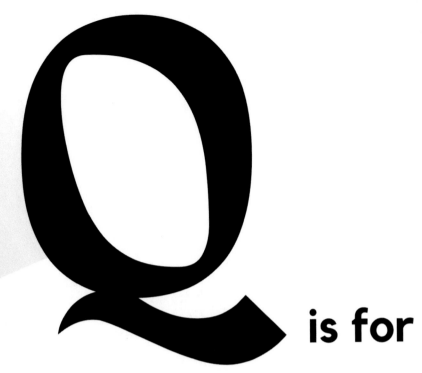

In Jamaica, we say guinep. Some are sour and some are sweet.

R is for

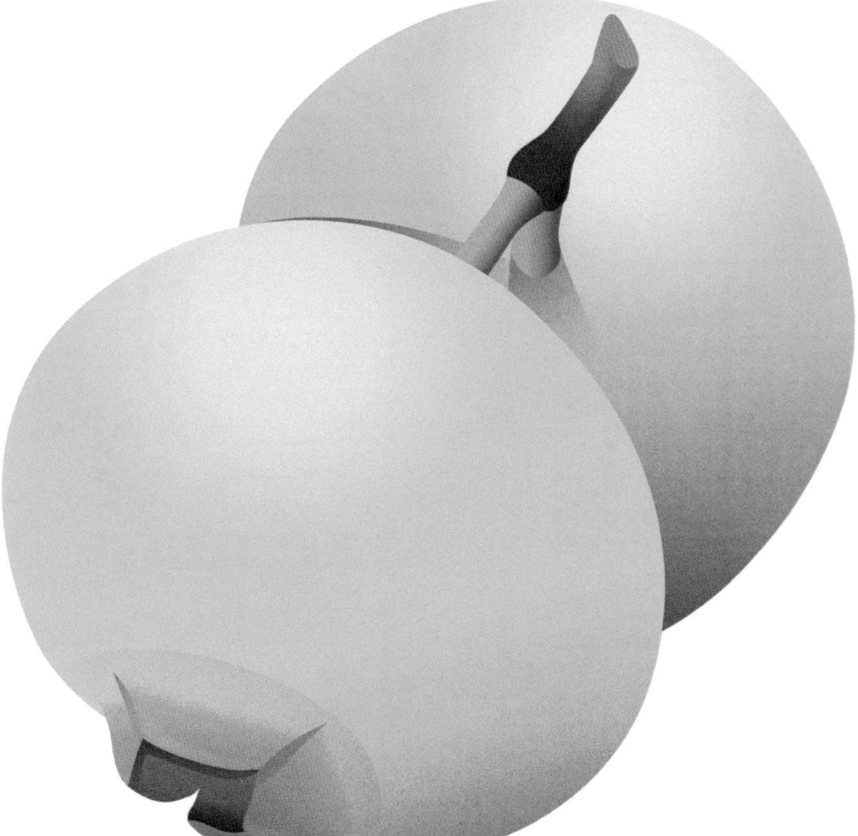

rose apple

They are such lovely treats.

S is for

star apple

S is for stinking toe.

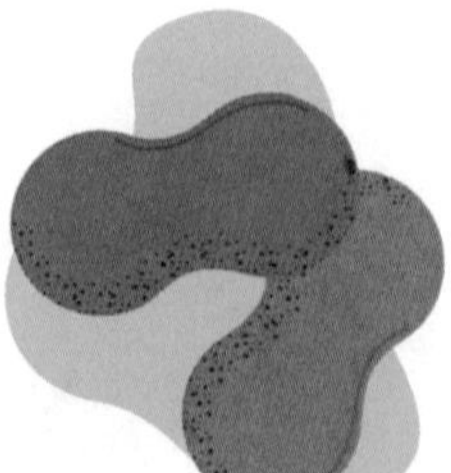

T is for

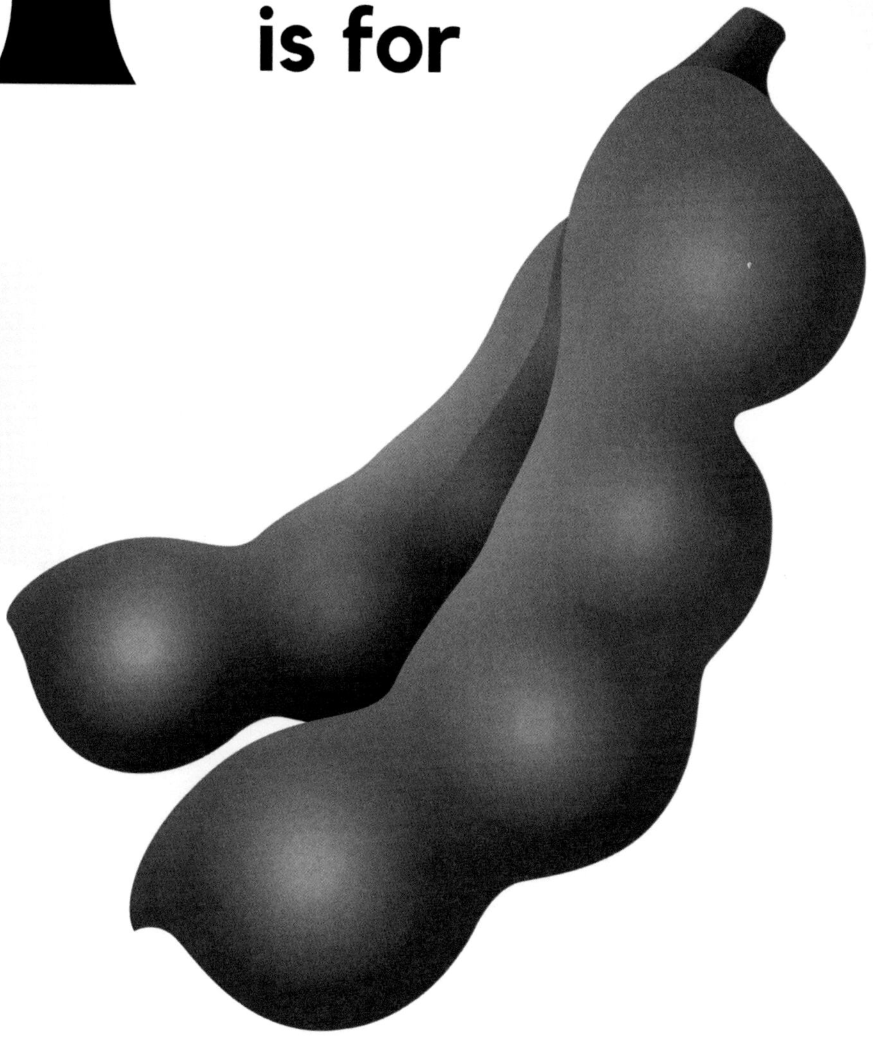

tamarind

Plant the seeds and watch them grow.

U is for

umbra fruits

Jamaican call them jew plum or June plum.

V is for

vanilla

This is the plant but we use it to make cake and ice cream. Yum!

W is for

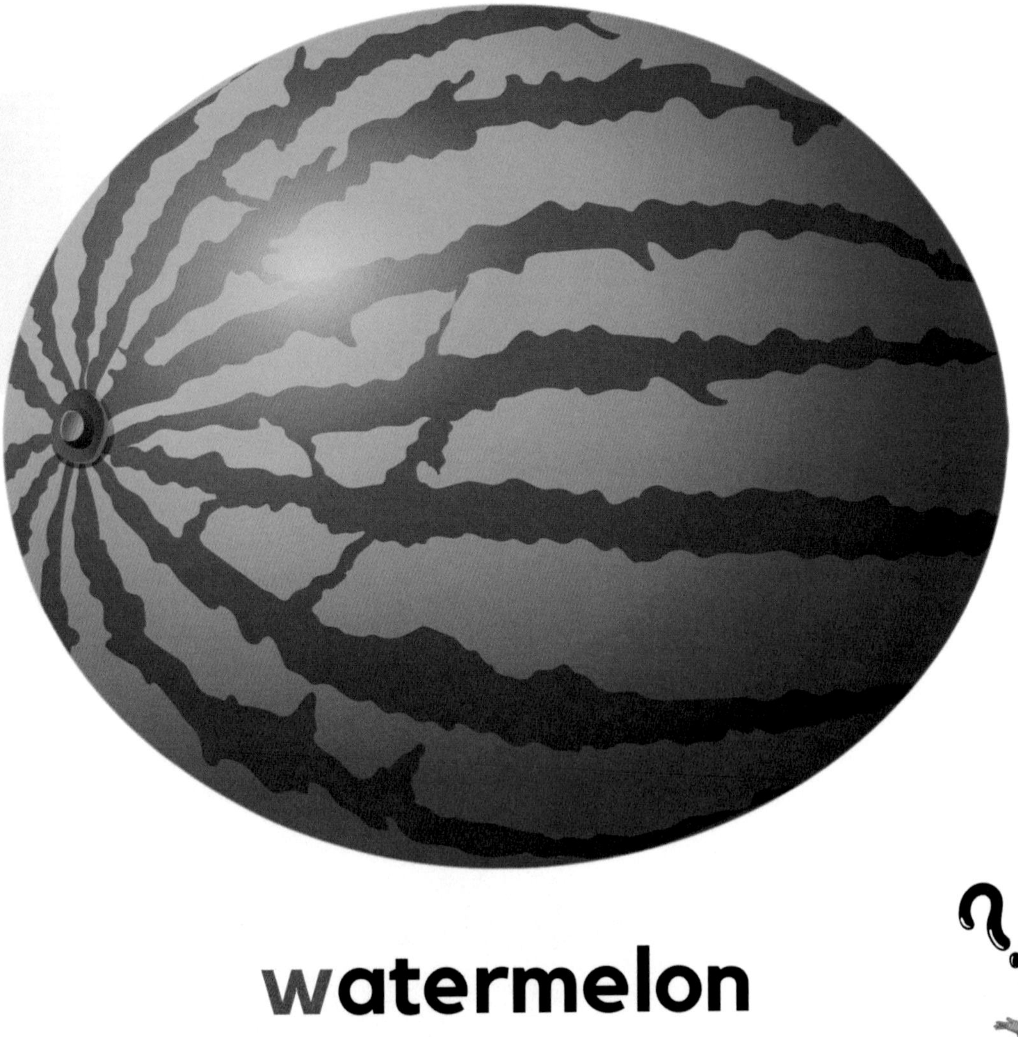

watermelon

Does this fruit have another name?

X is for

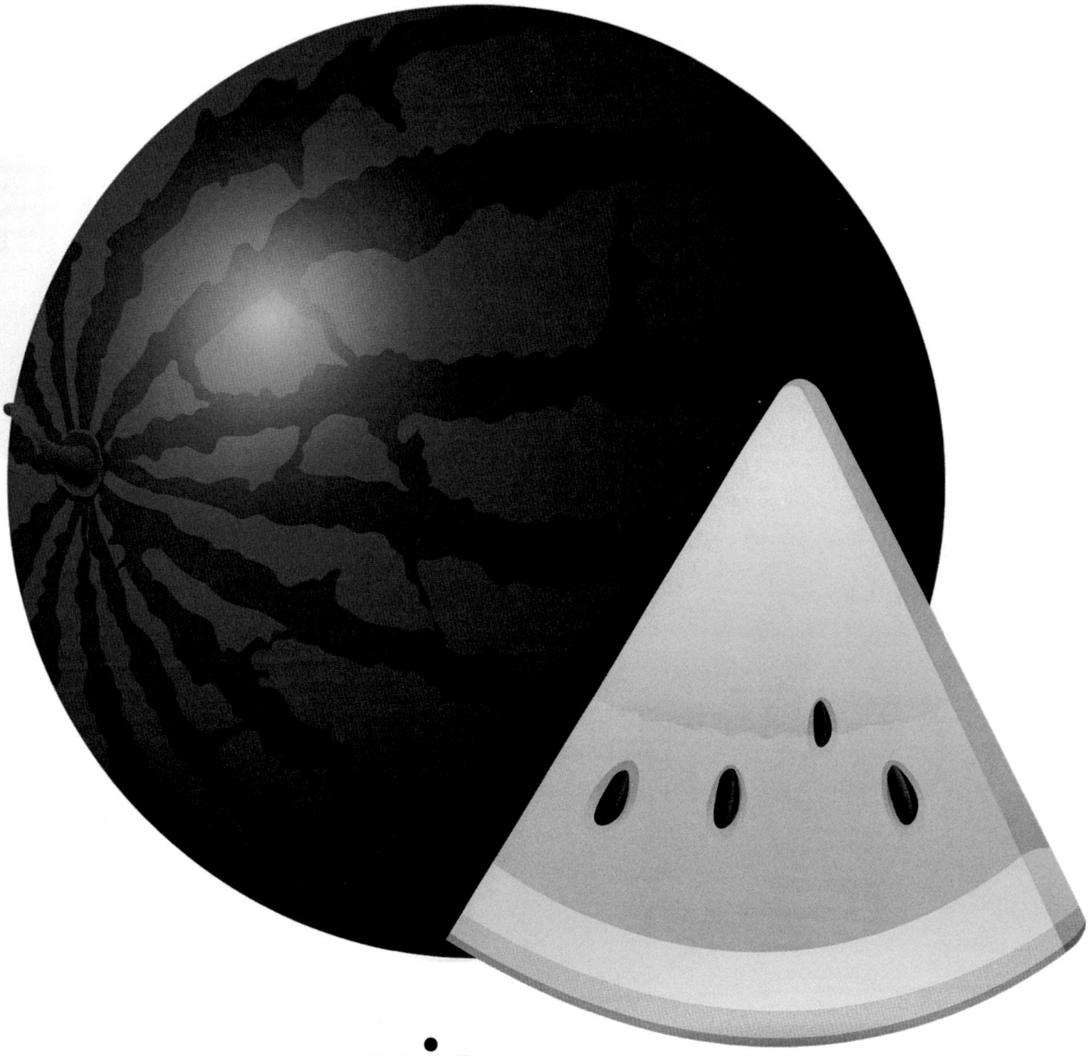

xigua

Watermelon and xigua are both the same.

Y is for

yam

We eat this in our soup.

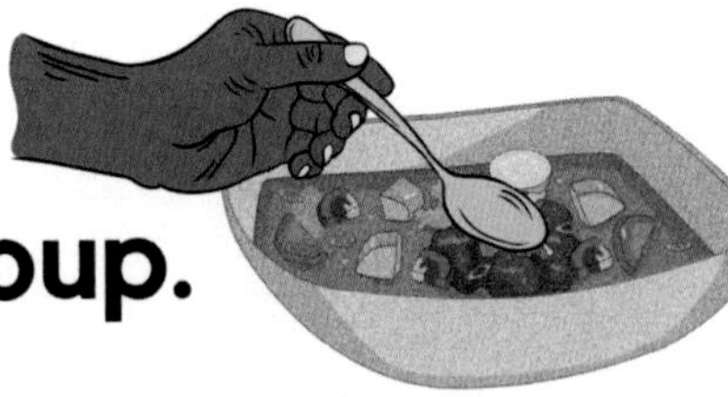

Z is for

zebra melon

Jamaicans call this canteloupe.

Aa
Ackee

Bb
Banana

Cc
Coconut

Dd
Dasheen

Ee
Elderberries

Ff
Fig

Gg
Guava

Hh
Hog plum

Ii
Ice cream

Jj
Jack fruit

Kk
Kidney beans

Ll
Lychee

Mm
Mango

Nn
Naseberry

Oo
Okra

Pp
Passion fruit

Qq
Quenepa

Rr
Rose apple

Ss
Star apple

Tt
Tamarind

Uu
Umbra fruit

Vv
Vanilla

Ww
Watermelon

Xx
Xigua

Yy
Yam

Zz
Zebra melon

SCAN ME

FOR MORE GAMES AND LEARNING

WWW.JAMAICANABC.COM
AUNTIEOLIVIA@JAMAICANABC.COM

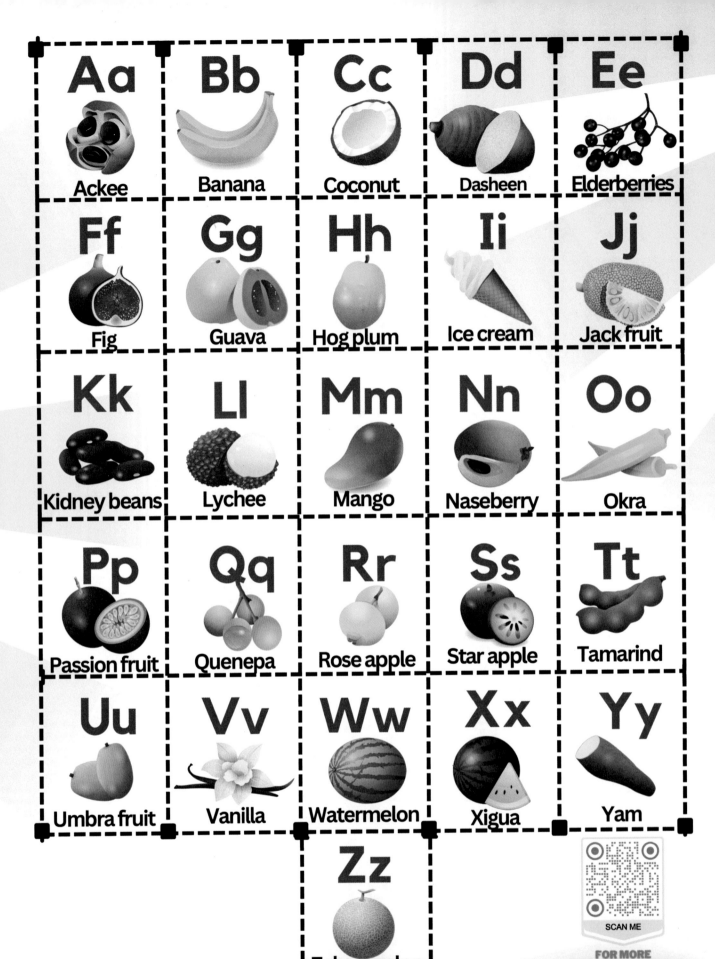

Made in the USA
Middletown, DE
11 April 2023

28673738R00018